Improving
Comprehension

for ages 9–10

A & C Black • London

Contents

*Extract from 'Magyk' by Angie Sage. Reproduced by permission of Bloomsbury.

**Extract from 'Building a shelter' by Gary Paulsen Reproduced by permission of Macmillan Children's Books.

Introduction

Improving Comprehension includes a range of interesting and exciting texts for sharing with pupils and using for reading comprehension. The texts have been carefully selected to be appropriate to the age group and to cover a range of text types. They reflect the demands of the Primary Framework for Literacy and in particular they following the learning objectives for Year 4. The accompanying comprehension worksheets are differentiated at three levels and are designed to be used by individuals or small groups. ***Notes for teachers*** are provided at the bottom of each worksheet providing guidance on how to get the most from the texts and how to approach the questions on the sheet.

For monitoring and recording purposes an ***Individual record sheet*** is provided on page 4 detailing reading and writing levels appropriate for Year 5. You may also find it helpful to refer to the ***Contents*** page where the 'texts' are linked to the relevant Assessment Focuses.

How to use the book and CD-ROM together

The book has fifteen 'texts', which can be projected on to a whiteboard for whole class use using the CD-ROM, or photocopied/printed for use with small groups or individuals. Sharing the text either on screen or on paper provides lots of opportunities for speaking and listening, for decoding words through a phonic approach, for reading and re-reading for meaning and for satisfaction and enjoyment in shared success.

For each text there are three comprehension worksheets at different ability levels to enable teachers to differentiate across the ability range. An animal picture at the top of the sheet indicates the level of the worksheet. The 'cat' exercises are at the simplest level; the 'dog' exercises are at the next level; the 'rabbit' exercises are at the most advanced level. You may decide to give some pupils the 'cat' worksheet and then decide, on the basis of their success, to ask them to complete the 'dog' worksheet. A similar approach could be taken with the 'dog' and 'rabbit' sheets.

After reading the text with the pupils the teacher should discuss the tasks with the children, ensuring that they understand clearly how to complete the worksheet and reminding them to answer the questions using full sentences and correct punctuation.

National Curriculum levels

The worksheets are aimed at the following ability levels:

Cat worksheets are for pupils working towards Level 3.
Dog worksheets are for pupils working confidently at Level 3.
Rabbit worksheets are for pupils who are working towards Level 4.

Individual record sheet

Pupil's name: _____

Date of birth: _____

Reading Level 3
- ☐ I can read a range of texts fluently and accurately.
- ☐ I can read independently.
- ☐ I use strategies appropriately to establish meaning.
- ☐ In my responses to fiction I show understanding of the main points and I express preferences.
- ☐ In my responses to non-fiction I show understanding of the main points and I express preferences.
- ☐ I know the order of the alphabet.
- ☐ I use my knowledge of the alphabet to locate books and find information.

Reading Level 4
- ☐ I can respond to a range of texts.
- ☐ I show understanding of significant ideas, themes, events and characters.
- ☐ I am beginning to use inference and deduction.
- ☐ I refer to the text when explaining my views.
- ☐ I can locate and use ideas and information.

Writing Level 3
- ☐ My writing is often organised, imaginative and clear.
- ☐ I use the main features of different forms of writing.
- ☐ I am beginning to adapt my writing to different readers.
- ☐ I use sequences of sentences to extend ideas logically.
- ☐ I choose words for variety and interest.
- ☐ The basic grammatical structure of my sentences is usually correct.
- ☐ My spelling is usually accurate, including that of common, polysyllabic words.
- ☐ I use punctuation accurately to mark sentences, including full stops, capital letters and question marks.
- ☐ My handwriting is joined and legible.

Writing Level 4
- ☐ I can write in a range of forms.
- ☐ My writing is lively and thoughtful.
- ☐ My ideas are often sustained and developed in interesting ways.
- ☐ My ideas are often organised appropriately for the purpose of the reader.
- ☐ My choice of vocabulary is often adventurous.
- ☐ I use words for effect.
- ☐ I am beginning to use grammatically complex sentences to extend meaning.
- ☐ My spelling, including that of polysyllabic words that conform to regular patterns, is generally accurate.
- ☐ I use full stops, capital letters and question marks are used correctly.
- ☐ I am beginning to use punctuation within the sentence.
- ☐ My handwriting is fluent, joined and legible.

FLOOD
Soaked School Stalls Start

The rainy days of June and July are still causing trouble. One school in the area is having to remain closed after the long summer holidays as it is still being cleared up after the floods.

Yesterday morning, angry parents gathered outside Beldon Primary School demanding to see the headteacher, Mr Brian Williams. The school should have reopened for the autumn term but parents and children arriving at school were met with a sign saying that the school was closed 'until further notice'.

"This is ridiculous," shouted one mum, Mel Brayley. "I got my kids dressed in their new uniform, we turned up at school and the teachers aren't even here."

"Our kids have been off all summer and we need to get them back to school," said harassed mother Martha Quidgly.

"Haven't they had a long enough holiday already?" asked furious father Dave Johnson. "I blame the head teacher. He can't seem to get anything organised. Surely it can't take two months to get a few soggy carpets taken out and replaced?"

Eventually Mr Williams did come out of the building to face the parents. He read out a short statement. "Obviously we are doing all we can to get things back to normal," he said. "At the moment it is too dangerous for children and staff to work in the school. The floods in late July swept through the buildings and in some places reached a depth of over a metre. It's not just damage to carpets but also to furniture, books and equipment. Even more seriously, however, the flood waters got into the electrical sockets and we are having all the electrics checked before we can allow children back into the buildings."

Mr Williams did not wait to answer any of the parents' questions and this enraged them further.

"It's not good enough," insisted Dave Johnson. "How long does it take to sort out a few electrics? Surely the County Council could get something done even if Brian Williams can't."

We contacted the Council but no one was available for comment. The school remains closed.

Andrew Brodie: Improving Comprehension for ages 9-10 © A&C Black Publishers Ltd 2008

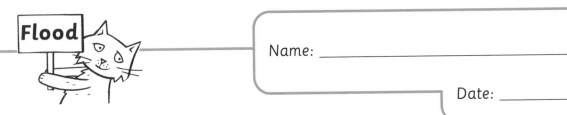

Flood

Name: _____

Date: _____

Answer the questions, using full sentences.

1. Why was the school closed?

    _____

    _____

2. What was the name of the headteacher?

    _____

    _____

3. What were the names of the parents who made angry comments?

    _____

    _____

4. Why were the parents angry?

    _____

    _____

5. Why would it be too dangerous for children to go to school?

    _____

    _____

6. Look around your classroom. What would be damaged if water flooded in to a depth of one metre?

    _____

    _____

    _____

    _____

    _____

    _____

Notes for teachers

Help the children to read this passage and talk about how it is written because it's in the style of a newspaper article. Discuss the questions with them and help them to write answers using correctly punctuated full sentences, by asking them to say their sentences out loud before writing them down. When considering the last question you could reassure the children that a flood is extremely unlikely. As an extension activity you could discuss the behaviour of the characters in this story. Discuss the title of the article : do the children notice the alliteration i.e. that all the words start with 's'? Do they know what the writer means by 'stalls'?

6

Andrew Brodie: Improving Comprehension for ages 9-10 © A&C Black Publishers Ltd 2008

Name: _____

Date: _____

Answer the questions, using full sentences.

1. How many parents made comments that were reported in the article?

    _____

    _____

2. When did the floods take place?

    _____

    _____

3. Why was Mel Brayley so cross?

    _____

    _____

4. What items did Mr Williams say had been damaged?

    _____

    _____

5. What was the most serious problem?

    _____

    _____

6. What would be the most serious problem if water flooded into your classroom?

    _____

    _____

    _____

    _____

    _____

    _____

Notes for teachers

Help the children to read this passage, asking them about the style and content of the newspaper article. When considering the last question you could reassure the children that a flood is extremely unlikely. As an extension activity you could discuss the behaviour of the characters in this story and see if the children can provide examples from the text to back up their ideas. Discuss the title of the article : do the children notice the alliteration i.e. that all the words start with 's'? Do they know what the writer means by 'stalls'?

Flood

Name: _____

Date: _____

Answer the questions using full sentences.

1. In what month would this article have appeared in the newspaper?

   _____

   _____

2. Approximately how long after the flood was the article written?

   _____

   _____

3. Approximately how long after the flood did Mr Johnson say it was?

   _____

   _____

   _____

4. Why did Mr Johnson blame the headteacher?

   _____

   _____

5. How did the parents feel after Mr Williams read out his statement?

   _____

   _____

6. Write a short description of how you would be affected if a flood happened in your school.

   _____

   _____

   _____

   _____

Notes for teachers
Help the children to read this passage and discuss how they know it is a newspaper article. Ensure that the children understand the sequence of events and the headline 'Soaked School Stalls Start'. When considering the last question you may wish to reassure the children that a flood is extremely unlikely. As an extension activity you could discuss the behaviour of the characters in this story: Did the parents behave well? Did the head teacher behave well? Did the writer of the article behave well i.e. was the writer being fair to the head teacher and the parents?

The letter from the head teacher

Beldon Church of England Primary School
Harborne Road, Beldon BE2 5DE

4th September 2008

Dear Parents,

I am writing to update you regarding the damage to the school caused by the recent floods.

Unfortunately, the school was seriously damaged by floodwater from the Beldon River when it overflowed on 29th July. As the school is on low-lying ground near the river a large quantity of water surged very rapidly through the school buildings. In classrooms 3 and 4 the water reached a depth of approximately one metre. I was in the school at the time and had to wade through the water to make my escape.

All the carpets in the school have had to be removed and are due to be replaced next week. The tables and chairs have had to be scrubbed clean as they were coated in a layer of mud. Qualified electricians are still checking the electrical circuits. The drainage systems have been checked to ensure that the sewage will be able to leave the buildings safely.

I am grateful to the many members of staff who have given up substantial time during the summer holidays to help with preparing the school for the new school year. Several parents have also been extremely helpful and I would like to offer my sincere thanks to them.

I am, however, dismayed and disappointed that some parents have chosen to complain to the local newspaper regarding the late opening of the school. I do hope that those people will now appreciate the substantial effort that has been made to make the school a pleasant and safe environment in which their children can work.

Yours sincerely,

Brian Williams

Brian Williams,
Headteacher

The letter from the head teacher

Name: _____

Date: _____

Answer the questions using full sentences.

1. Who wrote the letter?

   _____

   _____

2. On what date did he write the letter?

   _____

   _____

3. What town is the school in?

   _____

   _____

4. What road is the school in?

   _____

   _____

5. What happened to the school?

   _____

   _____

6. Write your school's address very carefully, as though you are writing it at the top of a letter.

   _____

   _____

   _____

   _____

   _____

   _____

Notes for teachers
This worksheet should be completed after 'Flood'. Help the children to read this passage, which is in the style of a letter. Point out how the letter is set out: the position of the address, date, etc. For the last question the children should write an introductory sentence such as *My school's address is as follows.*

Andrew Brodie: Improving Comprehension for ages 9-10 © A&C Black Publishers Ltd 2008

The letter from the head teacher

Name: _____

Date: _____

Answer the questions using full sentences.

1. What is the approximate age range of pupils in the school?

    _____

    _____

2. What is the postcode for the school? (Don't forget that your answer must be within a full sentence.)

    _____

    _____

3. Why did the headteacher write to the parents?

    _____

    _____

4. What was Mr Williams pleased about?

    _____

    _____

5. What was Mr Williams not pleased about?

    _____

    _____

6. Write your home address very carefully, as though you are writing it at the top of a letter.

    _____

    _____

    _____

    _____

    _____

    _____

Notes for teachers

This worksheet should be completed after 'Flood'. Help the children to read this passage and discuss the features that make it a letter. Point out how the letter is set out: the position of the address, date, etc. For the last question the children should write an introductory sentence such as *My home address is as follows.*

11

The letter from the head teacher

Name: _____

Date: _____

Answer the questions using full sentences.

1. What caused the school to flood?

   _____

   _____

2. Why were no children at school when it flooded?

   _____

   _____

3. How many days after the flood did Mr Williams write this letter?

   _____

   _____

   _____

4. List the problems that the flood caused to the school.

   _____

   _____

   _____

   _____

5. Imagine that you are one of the parents at the school. Write a letter to Mr Williams saying how you feel. You might be angry at the situation or you could be pleased with the way Mr Williams has dealt with it. Jot down some ideas on the lines below then use a clean piece of paper to create your letter.

   _____

   _____

   _____

   _____

   _____

   _____

Notes for teachers
This worksheet should be completed after 'Flood'. Help the children to read this passage and talk about the tone the head teacher is using. Is he cross, impatient, calm? What indicates this? Point out how the letter is set out: the position of the address, date, etc. For question 4 the children should write an introductory sentence such as *The flood caused the following problems in the school.*

Practising the piano

"Sit down and practise the piano."

"I just need to brush my hair," said Megan.

"All right, but do it straight after that."

"Of course I will," replied Megan with a smile.

Megan went upstairs and brushed her hair. Slowly. Then she decided she had to tidy her desk – that could take till lunchtime.

"Have you finished brushing your hair?" called a voice from downstairs.

"Yes, I just need to tidy my desk," Megan called back.

"That's a good idea, but make sure you do your piano practice," came the distant voice.

"Of course I will," Megan shouted back cheerily.

She turned back to her desk and saw her pencil case. It was full of pens, coloured pens, pencils, coloured pencils, a ruler, a folding ruler, two pencil sharpeners and a load of sharpenings. She decided it needed tidying too so she tipped it out on to the desk. Most of the pencils and coloured pencils needed sharpening so she set to work on them. She liked them really sharp and it took quite a long time.

"Lunchtime!" called the voice from below.

Megan jumped up and hopped her way downstairs. She ate her lunch … slowly.

Andrew Brodie: Improving Comprehension for ages 9-10 © A&C Black Publishers Ltd 2008

Name: _____

Date: _____

Answer the questions using full sentences.

1. What is the name of the girl in the story?

   _____

   _____

2. Who, do you think, is asking her to practise the piano?

   _____

   _____

3. Do you think that the girl wants to practise the piano?

   _____

   _____

4. What was the girl's first excuse to not practise the piano?

   _____

   _____

5. Which two things did the girl decide to tidy?

   _____

   _____

6. Make a list of all the things that you have in your pencil case.

   _____

   _____

   _____

   _____

   _____

   _____

Notes for teachers
Help the children to read this passage, pointing out the punctuation that is used to show speech. For the final task the pupils will need to make a list of items: remind them that items in a list are always separated by commas, except for the last two items where the word 'and' should be used. The purpose of the final task is to encourage children to look back at the text and see how a list sentence is structured. As an extra activity, ask the children to make a list of things they could do to avoid having to practise the piano/doing homework.

14

Practising the piano

Name: _____

Date: _____

Answer the questions, using full sentences.

1. Who do you think is telling Megan to practise the piano?

   _____

   _____

2. Why did Megan brush her hair slowly?

   _____

   _____

3. Why did Megan decide to tidy her desk and her pencil case?

   _____

   _____

4. Do you think that Megan is going to be in trouble for not practising the piano?

   _____

   _____

5. Do you think that Megan is behaving well?

   _____

   _____

6. Do you play a musical instrument? If you do, describe the instrument, your lessons and how often you practise. If you don't, describe which instrument you would like to play and why.

   _____

   _____

   _____

   _____

Notes for teachers
Help the children to read this passage, pointing out the punctuation that is used to show speech. The children may need some ideas and encouragement when approaching the final task on the worksheet. If they are not interested in playing an instrument then you could discuss playing a sport and what sort of practice they would need to do for that.

15

Practising the piano

Name: _____

Date: _____

Answer the questions using full sentences.

1. Look at the word 'practise'. Look through the passage carefully to find a different spelling of the word. Why is it spelt differently? You may need to look in a dictionary to help you with this question.

    _____

    _____

    _____

2. Why do you think Megan smiled when she said, 'Of course I will'?

    _____

    _____

3. How strict is the person who is asking Megan to practise, do you think?

    _____

    _____

4. What would you say to Megan to encourage her to practise?

    _____

    _____

    _____

5. How well behaved do you think Megan is?

    _____

    _____

6. What do you think happens next in the story? Does Megan ever practise the piano?

    _____

    _____

    _____

    _____

Notes for teachers

Help the children to read this passage discussing the punctuation that is used to show speech. Note that some of the questions could have more than one correct answer – we are simply asking the pupils to interpret the passage in their own way. The important thing about each answer is that it should be logical and sensible.

Martha's lazy day

In the passage below, ten year old Martha is on holiday with her parents and her younger brother Ned.

The family were having a lazy day. It was the third day of their stay in a villa on the Spanish coast. On day one, Monday, they had been to the beach; the next day they had driven up into the hills; and this, the third day had been declared a lazy day around the villa and its grounds. Martha was looking forward to a day enjoying the pool that was in the garden of their holiday home.

To add to the holiday fun, the family had bought a large inflatable gorilla that was now floating sedately around the swimming pool wearing a smug grin. Ned was shooting at it with a large water gun. To begin with he had aimed the super soaker at Martha and her parents but had been soundly told off and told to aim at nothing living.

In the middle of the afternoon, having climbed from the pool and smothered herself in sun cream, Martha chose a sun bed in a warm shady spot with the intention of reading her book. Though she was thoroughly enjoying the story about a well-known wizard, Martha soon found she was feeling drowsy in the warmth. She closed her eyes and enjoyed the sound of the water lapping against the tiled walls of the pool; the quiet chattering of the palm fronds as the gentle breeze moved them and the crickets making their maraca like sounds in the nearby pines. The world with its soothing sounds and comforting warmth lulled her into sleep.

The next thing Martha knew she was suddenly awake. For a moment she didn't know where she was and what had woken her. The world had gone cold dark and damp and something seemed to be resting on her.

For a split second pictures of her home and family dashed before her eyes where was she, why was she cold and how was she going to get out of here? She could feel herself panicking but then…

She leapt up to see the rest of the family all laughing at the result of Dad's dropping the very wet gorilla on top of her. At first Martha felt quite cross about her shock but soon saw the funny side of it.

The whole family enjoyed another dip in the pool before drying off in the warmth and dressing ready to go out for dinner. Martha had enjoyed her lazy day, or at least, she had enjoyed most of it.

Andrew Brodie: Improving Comprehension for ages 9-10 © A&C Black Publishers Ltd 2008

Martha's lazy day

Name: _____

Date: _____

Ring the correct answer for each of the following three questions.

1.   How many people were enjoying a holiday?

   two   three   four   five

2.   What country were they in?

   England   Spain   France   Germany

3.   What time of the day did Martha fall asleep on a sun bed?

   morning   afternoon   evening   night

Answer each of these questions with a simple sentence.

4.   Was Martha older or younger than Ned?

   Martha was _____

   _____

5.   What part of the day do you think Martha enjoyed the most?

   _____

   _____

6.   What did Dad drop on Martha while she was asleep?

   _____

   _____

7.   What sounds did Martha hear when she was lying on the sun bed?

   _____

   _____

   _____

   _____

Notes for teachers

All the words pupils need to use are in the questions or the text so it is important to encourage pupils to use correct spellings when writing their answers. The final question is so that pupils can appreciate that each of them will have used their own experiences and imaginations to envisage the scene that is being written about.

18

Martha's lazy day

Name: _____

Date: _____

Ring the correct answer for each of the following questions.

1. Which of the following is nearest in meaning to the word villa?

   hotel   holiday   house   habitat

2. What is meant by the term 'super soaker'?

   wet sponge   water gun   large bath   swimming pool

3. Which of the following words could be used to replace the word 'drowsy' in paragraph three.

   happy   unwell   sleepy   dizzy

Write a full sentence to answer each of the following questions.

4. Where was the pool that the family were enjoying?

   _____

   _____

5. What was Martha hoping to do when she sat down on the sun bed?

   _____

   _____

6. In your own words describe what woke Martha up.

   _____

   _____

   _____

   _____

   _____

   _____

   _____

   _____

Notes for teachers
Ensure the children have read and understood the passage, paying particular attention to any unfamiliar vocabulary. The first questions that invite pupils to ring the correct answers are designed to ensure they understand particular vocabulary within the text. Where pupils are asked to use their own words they should be encouraged to check spellings for accuracy.

19

Martha's lazy day

Name: _____

Date: _____

1. Ring the pair of words nearest in meaning to the word 'smug'.

    self satisfied   very happy   cheerfully warm

2. Ring the word nearest in meaning to 'lapping'.

    moving   slapping   turning

3. Which of the following is nearest in meaning to 'maraca'?

    beating noise   percussion   instrument   flying insect

Write a full sentence to answer each of the following questions.

4. How many different types of tree are mentioned in the text and what are they?

    _____

    _____

    _____

5. Explain what is meant, in the final sentence of the text, by the words 'or at least she had enjoyed most of it'?

    _____

    _____

    _____

6. Explain why Martha smothered herself in sun cream.

    _____

    _____

    _____

Notes for teachers
The first questions that invite pupils to ring the correct answers are designed to ensure they understand particular vocabulary within the text; they may need to use a dictionary to help with this task. The questions that demand written answers are to check they have understood certain phrases in the text.

20

Sun, Earth and Moon

The sun

The sun is a star. It is the nearest star to the earth. Several planets travel around the sun. We say they 'orbit' the sun. The planets, including Earth, Venus, Mercury, Mars, Saturn and Jupiter, form what is known as the 'solar system'*.

The earth

The earth is the planet on which we live and it is the only planet that can support life. The word 'earth' is sometimes written with a capital letter, Earth, especially when included in a list with the other planets of the solar system.

Two planets, Mercury and Venus, are closer to the sun than Earth is so we say that Earth is the third planet from the sun. The other planets are all further away from the sun than Earth is.

The earth is approximately 149,600,000 kilometres from the sun – that is 149.6 million kilometres. The diameter of the earth at the equator is 12,756 kilometres. Approximately three quarters of the earth is covered by water. The surface of the earth is called its crust.

The crust covers the layer called the mantle and the mantle surrounds the central part called the core.

The earth takes one day to spin around on its own axis and it takes one year to orbit the sun.

The moon

The moon is not a star and it is not a planet. It is a satellite of the earth – in other words it orbits the earth. The moon takes approximately one month to orbit the earth. The moon is approximately 384,000 kilometres from the earth. The diameter of the moon is 3,476 kilometres.

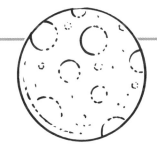

* The word solar means relating to the sun.

Andrew Brodie: Improving Comprehension for ages 9-10 © A&C Black Publishers Ltd 2008

Sun, Earth and Moon

Name: _____

Date: _____

Answer the questions, using full sentences.

1. Stars, planets and moons are known as celestial bodies. What type of celestial body is the sun?

    _____

2. What type of celestial body is the earth?

    _____

    _____

3. Give the names of three other planets in our solar system.

    _____

    _____

    _____

4. How far from the sun is the earth?

    _____

    _____

5. How far from the earth is the moon?

    _____

    _____

6. Find out the names of all the main planets in our solar system and make a list of them here – your list should be included within a sentence.

    _____

    _____

    _____

    _____

    _____

Notes for teachers

Help the children to read this non-fiction passage, ensuring that they understand it. Point out the use of a footnote, with the asterisk in the text indicating that the footnote is there. Help the pupils to find information for the last task, then to structure their list in a correctly punctuated sentence where the items in the list are separated by commas except for the last two where the word is used.

Andrew Brodie: Improving Comprehension for ages 9-10 © A&C Black Publishers Ltd 2008

Sun, Earth and Moon

Name: _____

Date: _____

Answer the questions using full sentences.

1. What does the word solar mean?

   _____

   _____

2. Which planets are closer to the sun than Earth is?

   _____

   _____

3. What is the diameter of the earth?

   _____

   _____

4. What is the diameter of the moon?

   _____

   _____

5. Use an encyclopaedia or the internet to find the answer to this question. What is the diameter of the sun?

   _____

   _____

6. Find the names of all the planets of the solar system and list them in the order of their distance from the sun.

   _____

   _____

   _____

   _____

   _____

Notes for teachers
Help the children to read this non-fiction passage, ensuring that they understand it. Do they know anything about our solar system? Point out the use of a footnote, with the asterisk in the text indicating that the footnote is there. Help the pupils to find information for the last task, then to structure their list in a correctly punctuated sentence where the items in the list are separated by commas except for the last two where the word 'and' is used.

Andrew Brodie: Improving Comprehension for ages 9-10 © A&C Black Publishers Ltd 2008

Sun, Earth and Moon

Name: _____

Date: _____

Answer the questions using full sentences.

1. When might we use a capital letter when writing the name of our planet?

   _____

   _____

2. The passage uses the term 'solar system'. Give another example of using the word solar and explain why it is used.

   _____

   _____

   _____

   _____

3. Find out which of the planets is closest to the sun.

   _____

   _____

4. How long does it take for the earth to orbit the sun?

   _____

   _____

5. How long does it take for the moon to orbit the earth?

   _____

   _____

6. This is a diagram of the earth shown as though a section has been removed. Use information from the passage to help you to label the diagram.

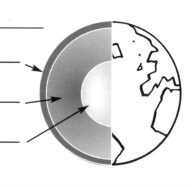

Notes for teachers

Help the children to read this non-fiction passage and see if they can recall any of the facts from it. Point out the use of a footnote, with the asterisk in the text indicating that the footnote is there. As an extra activity, pupils could research volcanos and earthquates in relation to the Earth's crust. Note that the word 'earth' is normally written without a capital letter and most dictionaries will show the other version – 'Earth' – as an alternative, especially where it is used with the names of the other planets. Some experts will advise that it should always appear with a capital when it is being used as an astronomical term. This makes an interesting point for discussion with pupils.

Victorian times

The following extract concerns a young boy called Robbie who has managed to travel back in time to the year 1875. He has met a girl called Charlotte who is showing him round the garden of her rather grand home.

They reached a clearing from where there was a wonderful view down to the house and to the river valley below it. Robbie stood still and looked and listened. It was so unbelievably different. There were lots more trees and between the clumps of trees there were small fields. Where he might have expected to see tractors there were horses, giant cart horses, led by burly farmers.

He couldn't see any roads. He could see hedges, between which roads might pass, but he couldn't see the roads themselves. He was sure he would be able to normally. Perhaps Mum would bring him to visit one day. That would surprise her, if he actually asked to visit a National Trust property. His usual reaction when she suggested such a thing was to sound horrified but then to go anyway as he felt that she needed the company.

Most amazing, though, was the silence. No, actually not silence. Robbie realised that he could hear birds, more than he would normally hear. He could hear the distant sounds of sheep baaing, cows mooing and, somewhere, an axe falling against timber. But what he couldn't hear was traffic: no tractors, no cars on the side roads, no lorries on the main road, no helicopters, no jets training for the Navy, no trains, no anything. It was stunning!

Robbie continued staring at the view. So green, so clear. There were farmhouses dotted about and a village in the distance. Over to the right was a small town. Very small but big enough to have a church, a ruined castle and a red-brick factory with a tall chimney from which smoke was rising.

"That's Father's factory," said Charlotte, following Robbie's gaze.

Andrew Brodie: Improving Comprehension for ages 9-10 © A&C Black Publishers Ltd 2008

Name: _____

Date: _____

Answer the questions, using full sentences.

1. What is the name of the boy who travelled back in time?

    _____

    _____

2. To which year did he travel?

    _____

    _____

3. What is the name of the girl he met?

    _____

    _____

4. What buildings could the boy see in the town?

    _____

    _____

5. Where were the children when the boy stopped to look at the view?

    _____

    _____

6. Make a list of the things that the boy thought were different from what he is used to.

    _____

    _____

    _____

    _____

    _____

    _____

Notes for teachers

Help the children to read this passage and ensure that they understand that Robbie has travelled back in time. When considering the last question encourage the children to reread the whole passage, perhaps underlining or highlighting the differences they found. When they are ready to answer the question, they should write an introductory sentence such as Robbie found the following differences between 1875 and the present day.

Victorian times

Name: _____

Date: _____

Answer the questions using full sentences.

1. To which year did Robbie travel back?

   _____

   _____

2. What is Charlotte showing Robbie?

   _____

   _____

3. What did Robbie see where he might have expected to see tractors?

   _____

   _____

4. Why were there no tractors?

   _____

   _____

5. What did Robbie find most amazing?

   _____

   _____

6. Make a list of the things that Robbie could hear and a list of the things that he couldn't hear.

   _____

   _____

   _____

   _____

   _____

   _____

Notes for teachers
Help the children to read this passage and ensure that they understand the story that Robbie has travelled back in time. How do they think this might have happened? When considering the last question encourage the children to reread the appropriate paragraph very carefully and to write the answer in their own words – in this way they are unlikely to miss anything. When they are ready to answer the question they should write an introductory sentence to each part, such as *Robbie could hear the following things*.

Andrew Brodie: Improving Comprehension for ages 9-10 © A&C Black Publishers Ltd 2008

Name: _____

Date: _____

Answer the questions using full sentences.

1. Who was the queen in 1875?

   _____

   _____

2. Charlotte's family owned the property in 1875. Who owns it now?

   _____

   _____

3. Why did Robbie want his mum to take him to visit the property again?

   _____

   _____

4. What did Robbie think there were more of in 1875 than in the present day?

   _____

   _____

5. How many years ago is 1875?

   _____

   _____

6. Look out of the window. Describe what your area might be like if you could travel back to see it in the year 1875.

   _____

   _____

   _____

   _____

   _____

   _____

   _____

Notes for teachers
Help the children to read this passage and ensure that they understand that Robbie has travelled back in time. Some children may not be aware of the work of the National Trust and the fact that the Trust owns many historical properties throughout the country. When considering the last question encourage the children to reread the whole passage, perhaps underlining or highlighting the differences they found. When they are ready to answer the question they should write an introductory sentence such as *Robbie found the following differences between 1875 and the present day.*

Andrew Brodie: Improving Comprehension for ages 9-10 © A&C Black Publishers Ltd 2008

The snowball-throwing sentry

The following extract is from the book Septimus Heap Magyk by Angie Sage. In this passage a young boy, who is a sentry guarding the tower where wizards live, has thrown a snowball that accidentally hit a very important wizard called Marcia.

Marcia looked at the snowball-throwing sentry. His hat was too big for him; it had slipped down and come to rest on his ears, which conveniently stuck out at just the right places to stop the hat from falling over his eyes. The hat gave the boy's thin, pinched face an unhealthy yellow tinge. His two deep grey eyes stared out from under it in terror as the boy realised that his snowball had hit the ExtraOrdinary Wizard.

He looked, thought Marcia, very small to be a soldier.

"How old are you?" she said accusingly.

The sentry blushed. No one like Marcia had ever looked at him before, let alone spoken to him.

"T-ten, Madam."

"Then why aren't you in school?" demanded Marcia.

The sentry looked proud. "I have no need of school, Madam. I am in the Young Army. We are the Pride of Today, the Warriors of Tomorrow."

"Aren't you cold?" Marcia asked unexpectedly.

"N-no Madam. We are trained not to feel the cold." But the sentry's lips had a bluish tinge to them, and he shivered as he spoke.

"Humph." Marcia stomped off through the snow, leaving the boy to another four hours on guard.

Andrew Brodie: Improving Comprehension for ages 9-10 © A&C Black Publishers Ltd 2008

The snowball-throwing sentry

Name: _____

Date: _____

Answer the questions using full sentences.

1. From what book does this passage come?

   _____

   _____

2. Who wrote the book?

   _____

   _____

3. What is the sentry guarding?

   _____

   _____

4. What is the name of the wizard?

   _____

   _____

5. How much longer did the sentry have to stay on guard?

   _____

   _____

6. Describe the sentry. You will need to read the passage again to find information about him.

   _____

   _____

   _____

   _____

   _____

   _____

   _____

   _____

Notes for teachers

Help the children to read this passage, ensuring that they understand that the ExtraOrdinary Wizard is Marcia. Can they remember any of the descriptive words that the author used to describe the sentry? Discuss the questions with them and help them to compose their answers orally before writing anything down. This will help with sentence structure and grammar.

Andrew Brodie: Improving Comprehension for ages 9-10 © A&C Black Publishers Ltd 2008

The snowball-throwing sentry

Name: _____

Date: _____

Answer the questions using full sentences.

1. What is the title of the book from which this passage comes and who wrote it?

   _____

   _____

2. What did the sentry do accidentally?

   _____

   _____

3. What special task were the sentry's ears achieving?

   _____

   _____

4. The sentry's eyes are grey. Which two other colours are mentioned in the passage and what are they describing?

   _____

   _____

   _____

5. Why doesn't the sentry go to school?

   _____

   _____

6. Describe the sentry in as much detail as you can. What does he look like? How old is he? What is he wearing? What job is he doing?

   _____

   _____

   _____

   _____

Notes for teachers
Help the children to read this passage and talk about how the author sets the scene. Can they find some examples of the language she uses? Encourage them to answer the questions out loud before writing anything down and to think about sentence structure and punctuation. The final question requires the children to look in several places in the passage.

Andrew Brodie: Improving Comprehension for ages 9-10 © A&C Black Publishers Ltd 2008

The snowball-throwing sentry

Name: _____

Date: _____

Answer the questions using full sentences.

1. Why do you think that the hat gave the boy's face a yellow tinge?

   _____

   _____

2. Why did the sentry blush?

   _____

   _____

   _____

3. How is the ExtraOrdinary Wizard speaking to the boy? Give examples of words that show us how she is speaking.

   _____

   _____

4. The boy says he is not cold but how has the writer shown us that he is?

   _____

   _____

5. Describe the sentry in as much detail as you can. Consider how he feels.

   _____

   _____

   _____

   _____

   _____

6. What other books has Angie Sage written? You may need to look on the internet to find the answer to this question.

   _____

   _____

Notes for teachers

Help the children to read this passage, ensuring that they understand that the ExtraOrdinary wizard is Marcia. The fifth question is very challenging particularly in relation to how the sentry feels – encourage the children to notice that, in addition to his feeling of coldness, his emotional feelings are referred to in two other places in the passage.

Andrew Brodie: Improving Comprehension for ages 9-10 © A&C Black Publishers Ltd 2008

Manners

If you think these boys sound like some that you know this could be a coincidence – but perhaps it isn't!

Scott Rill, Ben King and Kenny Spanners
Were three young men, who lacked in manners.
They treated school as quite a laugh
Barely listened to teaching staff.
(Who by the way really did despair
Hence had prematurely greying hair.)

One day, when arriving as normal at school,
Not surprisingly, playing the fool.
They thought, 'what fun to be last into class',
So when the bell went let all others pass.
Then stayed in the cloakrooms, the mischievous bunch
Lingered a while, eating someone's packed lunch.

Ten minutes later they thought they would stroll
Back into class, (still chewing cheese roll!)
They went self assuredly in with a swagger,
But the sight that they saw nearly caused them to stagger.
The classroom was empty, noone was there,
No children to giggle, no teacher to stare.

What should they do, where should they go?
Where was their class? They'd all like to know.
Scott, Ben and Kenny turned round and saw,
To their shock, the head teacher just there by the door.
Suddenly, feeling far less than most bold,
They tried their best to look as good as gold.

"Deliberately late, you know the rules.
Even though you act like fools.
It's far too late to look contrite
Just because you've had a fright.
If you had come in, on time, looking neat
Like your classmates, you'd be enjoying a treat.

Your class have all gone, with of course your fine teacher
Into the hall for a special feature.
Some famous celebrities are with us today
T.V. cameras are filming their stay.
Everything has now already begun
It's too late for you to join in the fun".

"Never mind," said the head, with a smile on his face.
"I'm sure that for you, I can find a good place
For the day to be spent in a hardworking way,
You can work in Year One, just for today.
I feel sure you'll fit in wonderfully well,
Learning to count, to read and to spell."

He wouldn't listen to the three boys' pleading
That they would rather be in the library, reading.
He led them down to the class of Year One
With plenty of work that had to be done.
As they each sat down on a very small chair
He heard them mutter that it just wasn't fair!

It sounds fair to me – all actions have consequences. I wonder if these three boys learned anything that day!

Andrew Brodie: Improving Comprehension for ages 9-10 © A&C Black Publishers Ltd 2008

Name: _____

Date: _____

Ring the correct answer for each of the following three questions.

1. How many boys are named in the poem?

    one   two   three   four

2. Where did the poem take place?

    hospital   school   home   cinema

3. Where did the boys spend the day?

    In Year One   In Year Two   In Year Three   In Year Four

The following questions should be answered with a simple sentence. The first one has been started for you.

4. In verse two, what are we told the three boys thought?
    The boys thought it would be fun to be

    _____ .

5. Where did the boys stay when the other children went into their classroom?

    _____

    _____

6. Who stood by the door of the empty classroom?

    _____

    _____

7. Copy the line from the poem that tells you who the special visitors to the school were.

    _____

    _____

Notes for teachers
Ensure the children have read and understood the poem, paying particular attention to any unfamiliar vocabulary. All the words pupils need to use are in the questions or the text so it is important to encourage pupils to use correct spellings when writing their answers. When answering the last question the pupils should carefully copy the third line of verse six.

Andrew Brodie: Improving Comprehension for ages 9-10 © A&C Black Publishers Ltd 2008

Manners

Name: _____

Date: _____

1. Ring the word that best describes the three boys.

    naughty   reliable   curious   heroic

2. Ring the word nearest in meaning to 'stroll'.

    rush   amble   crawl   hop

Write a full sentence to answer each of the following questions.

3. How did pupils at the school in the poem know when it was time to go in?

    _____

    _____

4. How do you think the boys felt when they walked into an empty classroom?

    _____

    _____

5. Why do you think the boys pleaded to be allowed to read in the library?

    _____

    _____

6. Match the first half of each sentence with the correct second half, then write them in the correct order, on a separate piece of paper to tell the story of the poem.

Instead they had to spend the day	badly behaved at school.
One morning they hung about	with the Year One children.
Scott, Ben and Kenny were	a treat enjoyed by the rest of the class.
They had missed the start of	in the cloakroom before going into class.

Notes for teachers

The first questions that invite pupils to ring the correct answers are designed to ensure they understand particular vocabulary within the text. The other questions should always be answered in correctly written and, where appropriate, detailed sentences. When tackling the final task, encourage pupils to present the sentences with care within a paragraph. Children should understand that they don't need to begin each sentence on a new line.

Name: _____

Date: _____

1. Ring the word nearest in meaning to 'premature'.

    paler   early   long   surprisingly

2. Which of the following is nearest in meaning to 'lingered'?

    hid   messed about   waited around   ate lunch

3. Which two of the following are nearest in meaning to the word 'contrite'?
    (Ring two words.)

    remorseful   frightened   repentant   shocked

Write a full sentence to answer each of the following questions.

4. In verse seven it says that the head teacher was smiling; explain why you
    think this was the case.

    _____

    _____

    _____

5. On the last line of the poem the boys are heard to mutter that it just isn't
    fair. Explain why you think they feel this way and why they only mutter
    rather than speaking out loud and clear.

    _____

    _____

    _____

6. At the beginning and end of the poem there are sentences in italics. What
    do you think is the purpose of these?

    _____

    _____

    _____

Notes for teachers
Read the poem aloud together, emphasizing the rhyme and rhythm. Do the children like the poem? Do they
think the boys are being treated fairly? If not what sort of punishment do they think is appropriate?

36

The chase

Larry ducked down behind the wall where the boys couldn't see him. It was good to have a chance to get his breath back. The chase had been totally exhausting and he had the feeling that it wasn't over yet. He breathed deeply and tried to relax but every muscle in his body seemed to be aching. Still, he could put up with the pain … if he could get away.

The boys were searching the ground lower down the slope. Larry could hear them crashing around, beating the bracken with sticks. He didn't dare look, not even a peep over the wall, as those sticks could be beating him instead of the bracken.

Larry decided he should move. It would be safer with more ground between him and them. Besides, they would find the track that led up the slope soon.

He stretched out his legs and wriggled his toes, then gently revolved his feet to prepare his ankles. The slope further up was covered with loose stones and the last thing he wanted was to twist his ankle.

He looked up at the stones on the slope to try to plan his route. He would have to be careful not to get part way up then simply slide back down again. That would make too much noise as well. There was a spindly tree near the bottom left of the slope. If he could reach that he could pull himself up then push himself on towards the next tree, a bigger one that he could hide behind if need be. Then there was an open patch with no trees, just stones and some odd roots from the trees higher up – that would be tricky but it was only a few metres and he might be able to do that on his hands and knees, grabbing hold of the roots where he could. Beyond that, he would reach the safety of the woods. He would be fine then, because there was plenty of shelter.

Being careful not to allow his head to be seen above the low wall, Larry eased himself up to a squatting position. He turned towards the wall to pick up his bag then turned round again ready to start the climb. His face was suddenly level with a pair of heavy boots.

"Where do you think you're going Larry?" The voice was full of menace.

Larry sank back and held his head in his hands.

Andrew Brodie: Improving Comprehension for ages 9-10 © A&C Black Publishers Ltd 2008

The chase

Name: _____

Date: _____

Answer the questions using full sentences.

1. Why did Larry hide behind the wall?

_____

_____

2. Why was he so tired?

_____

_____

3. Where were the other boys?

_____

_____

4. Where did Larry want to go next?

_____

_____

5. Why did Larry turn to face the wall?

_____

_____

6. What did he see when he turned back again?

_____

_____

7. Why do you think Larry is trying to hide from the other boys? Try to describe what you think has happened before.

_____

_____

_____

_____

Notes for teachers
Read the passage with the children and talk about how the author creates tension in the story. Do they know at the beginning who Larry is running away from? Why do they think he was being chased? Discuss the answer to question 7 with the children before they write anything down.

38

The chase

Name: _____

Date: _____

Answer the questions, using full sentences.

1. What advantages did Larry gain by hiding behind the wall?

   _____

   _____

2. How did Larry know where the boys were?

   _____

   _____

3. How did Larry prepare to make his next move?

   _____

   _____

4. In what ways did Larry know that he would have to be careful in tackling the next slope?

   _____

   _____

5. What did Larry have with him?

   _____

   _____

6. Use your own ideas in answering this question. Who do you think has approached Larry and what will happen next?

   _____

   _____

   _____

   _____

   _____

   _____

Notes for teachers
Help the children to read this passage and talk about the sequence of events in the story. Why do they think Larry is being chased? What is he scared of? Have they every had a similar experience that they can tell you about?

39

The chase

Name: _____

Date: _____

Answer the questions, using full sentences and using your own words as much as possible.

1. Why didn't Larry dare look over the wall?

    _____

    _____

2. What was the tree near the bottom of the slope like?

    _____

    _____

3. Describe how Larry planned to get up the slope.

    _____

    _____

    _____

4. What does the writer mean by 'the voice was full of menace'?

    _____

    _____

5. How must Larry have felt when he 'sank back and held his head in his hands'?

    _____

    _____

6. Help Larry to escape! Write the next part of the story.

    _____

    _____

    _____

    _____

    _____

    _____

Notes for teachers
The final task is to extend the story – depending on the time available, you may like the pupils to write a short paragraph giving some detail of the next thing that happens to Larry or you could ask them to use the six lines above for notes before they embark on a longer follow-up.

Charles Kingsley (1819 – 1875)

The author Charles Kingsley was an Anglican Clergyman as well as a talented writer.

Whilst some of his written works were for adults he also wrote stories for children. He would, on occasions, write under another name (this is called a pseudonym), that of 'Parson Lot'. Much of Kingsley's writing was done to encourage people to think about the very poor living conditions that many people endured in Victorian Britain. Kingsley was very concerned about the lack of education for girls at the time and the terrible working conditions, particularly as some of the workers were young children.

Amongst his works for children is the fairy tale for which he is best remembered, 'The Water Babies'. In this story the central character is Tom, a young boy who works as a chimney sweep but soon becomes a 'water baby' living under the water. This tale was first seen in 1862 as a serial in a magazine. The following year it was published as a book.

In 1874 Charles Kingsley spent a very tiring six months touring the United States of America and died on 23rd January the following year.

Sweeping Chimneys

Chimneys need to be cleaned regularly as a layer of black soot builds up in them. In the past the sweeping of chimneys was a difficult and dangerous job. In large houses it was not uncommon for boys as young as five to be sent up into the chimneys to clean them. These children would have to crawl up the square flues, which were only about twenty centimetres wide. The 'climbing boys' as they were sometimes known were poorly fed to keep them thin enough to fit up the chimneys. In some houses, there were several chimneys that would meet part of the way up to form one big chimney. Due to the many twists and turns, children could occasionally get lost or even suffocate up there.

The 'climbing boys' had masters who forced them to do this dangerous job every day. As you might imagine, the young boys involved didn't enjoy the work and were often very reluctant to leave the fireplaces to enter/climb the perilous chimneys. To make sure the children went up into the flue their masters would sometimes light a small fire in the hearth so the boys had to scramble up the chimney to avoid being burned. If the chimney flue was too narrow then the boys could become stuck and being unable to move would die where they were.

During the reign of Queen Victoria, laws were passed forbidding the cruel practice of using young boys to sweep chimneys and now chimney-sweeps use brushes to clean the chimneys.

Andrew Brodie: Improving Comprehension for ages 9-10 © A&C Black Publishers Ltd 2008

Name: _____

Date: _____

Ring the correct answer for each of the following three questions.

1. In which year was Charles Kingsley born?

   1819   1964   1875   1915

2. What is the title of a famous fairy tale he wrote?

   Victorian Britain   Tom   Clergyman   The Water Babies

3. What could happen to a climbing boy in a very narrow chimney flue?

   He could sing a song.   He could get stuck.

   He could twist and turn.   He could read a book.

The following questions should be answered with a simple sentence. The first one has been started for you.

4. How long did Kingsley spend touring the U.S.A.?
   Kingsley spent _____

5. What were the boys who went into chimneys sometimes called?

   _____

   _____

6. What is used nowadays to sweep a chimney?

   _____

   _____

   _____

   _____

Notes for teachers
Ensure the children have read and understood the passage and talk about the connections between the two pieces of writing. All the words that pupils need to use are in the questions or the text so it is important to encourage pupils to check their spelling when writing their answers. Discuss the similarities and differences between the two pictures with the children before they make a choice.

Andrew Brodie: Improving Comprehension for ages 9-10 © A&C Black Publishers Ltd 2008

Charles Kingsley (1819 – 1875)

Name: _____

Date: _____

Ring the correct answer for each of the following questions.

1. In which year was 'The Water Babies' published as a book?

    1862   1863   1864   1865

2. For whom did Charles Kingsley write 'The Water Babies'?

    adults   girls   adults and children   children

Write a full sentence to answer each of the following questions.

3. What were the two careers that Charles Kingsley had?

    _____

    _____

4. In which country did Kingsley spend six months the year before he died?

    _____

    _____

5. Why were young, poorly fed children made to climb up the chimneys?

    _____

    _____

6. Explain in your own words why you think it was important that a law was passed to prevent children from having to clean chimneys.

    _____

    _____

    _____

    _____

    _____

    _____

Notes for teachers
Ensure the children have read and understood the passage, paying particular attention to any unfamiliar vocabulary e.g. 'flue'. Do they see how the two passages are related? Have they heard any other stories about what children were made to do in Victorian times e.g. the Little Match Girl.

Andrew Brodie: Improving Comprehension for ages 9-10 © A&C Black Publishers Ltd 2008

Charles Kingsley (1819 – 1875)

Name: _____

Date: _____

Ring the correct answer for each of the following questions.

1. Which of the following words is nearest in meaning to 'perilous'?

    difficult   dirty   delicate   dangerous

2. Another name Kingsley used when writing was

    Charles Kingsley   Parson Lot   Anglican Clergyman

3. What type of story is 'The Water Babies'?

    Fable   Myth   Legend   Fairy Tale

Write a full sentence to answer each of the following questions.

4. What might a young sweep's master do to encourage him to enter a chimney?

    _____

    _____

5. What is a pseudonym?

    _____

    _____

6. Explain the purpose behind all Charles Kingsley's writing.

    _____

    _____

    _____

7. Imagine that you were a climbing boy. On a separate sheet of paper write about your experiences.

Notes for teachers
Discuss the passages with the children and talk about Charles Kingsley and what he did. Do they know what this type of writing is called? (A biography). You might need to explain what a pseudonym is and why authors might use one. For question 6, pupils should understand that all Charles Kingsley's written works were to make people aware of the poor living conditions endured by both adults and children.

The Water Babies

The following three extracts are from the first chapter of 'The Water Babies' by Charles Kingsley. The first two extracts tell you a little about Tom and his way of life and the final one concerns his work in the chimneys of a large country house.

Extract 1

Once upon a time there was a little chimney-sweep, and his name was Tom. That is a short name, and you have heard it before, so you will not have much trouble in remembering it. He lived in a great town in the North country, where there were plenty of chimneys to sweep, and plenty of money for Tom to earn and his master to spend. He could not read nor write, and did not care to do either; and he never washed himself, for there was no water up the court where he lived.

Extract 2

He cried half his time, and laughed the other half. He cried when he had to climb the dark flues, rubbing his poor knees and elbows raw; and when the soot got into his eyes, which it did every day in the week; and when he had not enough to eat, which happened every day in the week likewise. And he laughed the other half of the day, when he was tossing half-pennies with the other boys, or playing leap-frog over the posts, or bowling stones at the horses' legs as they trotted by, which last was excellent fun, when there was a wall at hand behind which to hide.

Extract 3

And then the housekeeper turned them into a grand room, all covered up in sheets of brown paper, and bade them begin, in a lofty and tremendous voice; and so after a whimper or two, and a kick from his master, into the grate Tom went, and up the chimney, while a housemaid stayed in the room to watch the furniture; to whom Mr. Grimes paid many playful and chivalrous compliments, but met with very slight encouragement in return.

How many chimneys he swept I cannot say: but he swept so many that he got quite tired, and puzzled too, for they were not like the town flues to which he was accustomed, but such as you would find – if you would only get up them and look, which perhaps you would not like to do – in old country-houses, large and crooked chimneys, which had been altered again and again, till they ran into one another. So Tom fairly lost his way in them; not that he cared much for that, though he was in pitchy darkness, for he was as much at home in a chimney as a mole is underground; but at last, coming down as he thought the right chimney, he came down the wrong one, and found himself standing on the hearthrug in a room the like of which he had never seen before.

Andrew Brodie: Improving Comprehension for ages 9-10 © A&C Black Publishers Ltd 2008

The Water Babies

Name: _____

Date: _____

Ring the correct answer for each of the following questions.

1. Name the young chimney sweep in the story.

    Tim   Tom   Ted   Tony

2. What got into his eyes every day?

    chimneys   water   stones   soot

3. What was the name of Tom's master?

    Mr Grimes   Mrs Grimes   Housekeeper   Charles Kingsley

Each of the following questions should be answered with a simple sentence. The first one has been started for you.

4. What are we told Tom never did?

    Tom never _____

5. Where did Tom play leap-frog?

    _____

    _____

6. Who wrote the story of 'The Water Babies'?

    _____

    _____

7. What was special about the chimneys in the old country houses?

    _____

    _____

    _____

    _____

    _____

Andrew Brodie: Improving Comprehension for ages 9-10 © A&C Black Publishers Ltd 2008

The Water Babies

Name: _____

Date: _____

Ring the correct answer for each of the following questions.

1. From which part of the 'Water Babies' story do you think the extracts were taken?

    the beginning   the middle   the final chapter   the first chapter

2. How much of the time are we told that Tom spent crying?

    often   half the time   all the time   never

3. Circle the word used to describe the inside smoke duct of a chimney.

    flu   flue   grate   sweep

Write a full sentence to answer each of the following questions.

4. Which words in the first extract tell you that Tom was not concerned about his inability to read or write?

    _____

    _____

    _____

5. How often was Tom hungry because he hadn't had enough to eat?

    _____

    _____

    _____

6. Why do you think a housemaid stayed in the room to watch the furniture?

    _____

    _____

    _____

Notes for teachers

Ensure the children have understood the passages and that they are taken from three different parts of the Water Babies book. In question 3 you may need to discuss the words 'smoke duct' with the children. The other questions should always be answered in correctly punctuated and, where appropriate, detailed sentences.

Andrew Brodie: Improving Comprehension for ages 9-10 © A&C Black Publishers Ltd 2008

The Water Babies

Name: _____

Date: _____

1. Ring the word nearest in meaning to 'chivalrous'.

    churlish   gentlemanly   unkind   false

2. Which word is nearest in meaning to 'bowling'?

    throwing   running   bouncing   holding

3. Which of the following is nearest in meaning to the word 'grate'?

    grill   fireplace   chimney stack   coal bucket

Write a full sentence to answer each of the following questions.

4. Explain what is meant in the first extract by the words 'plenty of money for Tom to earn and his master to spend.'

    _____

    _____

    _____

5. Why do you think the grand room described in the third extract is said to be 'all covered up in sheets of brown paper' and what exactly would have been covered?

    _____

    _____

    _____

6. Explain what is meant in the third extract by 'he was as much at home in a chimney as a mole is underground'.

    _____

    _____

    _____

Notes for teachers

The last set of questions involves interpretation so you might need to discuss these with the children before they write anything down. In the fifth question it's important that pupils realise that the objects covered in the room would be the furnishings and possibly rugs – not the whole room as stated in the extract.

48

Television

Most homes, though not all, have at least one television. Many homes have several televisions, with perhaps one in the lounge, one in the kitchen and one in each bedroom. For most of us life without the television would be very strange. A hundred years ago nobody had televisions in their homes at all – televisions as we know them simply had not been invented.

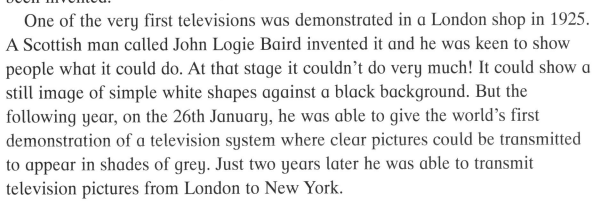

One of the very first televisions was demonstrated in a London shop in 1925. A Scottish man called John Logie Baird invented it and he was keen to show people what it could do. At that stage it couldn't do very much! It could show a still image of simple white shapes against a black background. But the following year, on the 26th January, he was able to give the world's first demonstration of a television system where clear pictures could be transmitted to appear in shades of grey. Just two years later he was able to transmit television pictures from London to New York.

The BBC made its first public television broadcast in 1936 but had to close its television service in 1939 because of the start of the Second World War. Although the war ended in 1945, the BBC did not start broadcasting again until 1946. Most people in those days couldn't afford a television set and it was not until a special event took place in 1953 that television became popular.

The special event was the Coronation of Queen Elizabeth the second and everybody wanted to be able to watch this. Those who could afford it bought a television set while those who couldn't afford one visited friends to watch theirs.

With television gaining in popularity, new companies were set up to broadcast television programmes. By the end of the 1950s most people had the choice of two channels to watch on their televisions: BBC or ITV. On both channels, programmes were only shown for part of the day and for the evening.

Up until the 1960s all television broadcasts in this country were in black and white. This meant that people, scenery and countryside appeared in shades of grey. By the end of that decade broadcasts were being made in full colour, though many people couldn't see the colours as their televisions could only receive black and white pictures!

Today we have a huge choice of television channels. We can watch them all in colour and we can watch at any time of day. We can record programmes to watch later and we can even use our televisions to play games on. Televisions have changed considerably since the first broadcasts so many years ago.

Andrew Brodie: Improving Comprehension for ages 9-10 © A&C Black Publishers Ltd 2008

Television

Name: _____

Date: _____

Answer the questions, using full sentences.

1. How many televisions do you have at home?

    _____

    _____

2. Why would you not have had a television if you had lived a hundred years ago?

    _____

    _____

3. What was the name of the man who demonstrated one of the first types of television?

    _____

    _____

4. What country did the man come from?

    _____

    _____

5. What special event encouraged people to buy their first television?

    _____

    _____

6. Describe what you would do at home if you didn't have a television.

    _____

    _____

    _____

    _____

    _____

    _____

Television

Name: _____

Date: _____

Answer the questions, using full sentences.

1. In which rooms in your house do you have a television?

    _____

    _____

2. In which year did John Logie Baird demonstrate his television in a London shop?

    _____

    _____

3. How had he improved his television by the following year?

    _____

    _____

4. Why did the BBC close down its television service for several years?

    _____

    _____

5. In which decade did colour television become available in this country?

    _____

    _____

6. Most people in this country didn't have television until the 1950s. What do you think people did in the evenings to amuse themselves?

    _____

    _____

    _____

    _____

Notes for teachers
Help the children to read this passage and then see if they can remember any of the key facts. The final question is extremely tricky and you may like to give the pupils ideas such as: listening to the radio, playing board games, reading, making things, drawing pictures, etc. As an extension activity you could discuss the fututre of television. Will they continue to change? How will they change?

Andrew Brodie: Improving Comprehension for ages 9-10 © A&C Black Publishers Ltd 2008

Television

Name: _____

Date: _____

Answer the questions, using full sentences.

1. Who transmitted television pictures from London to New York in 1928?

_____

_____

2. When did the BBC make its first television broadcast?

_____

_____

3. Give two reasons why you would not have bought a television in 1942.

_____

_____

4. You could look in a TV listings magazine or in a newspaper to see the television schedules for ideas. List at least six different types of television programme.

_____

_____

_____

_____

5. Imagine that television had never been invented. How would life be better for you and how would life be worse for you?

_____

_____

_____

_____

_____

_____

Notes for teachers

Help the children to read this passage and then discuss some of the main events. The final two tasks are quite demanding and the pupils may need some support with their ideas and how best to phrase them. As always, encourage them to use correct punctuation and spelling in their answers.

Building a shelter

The text below is from 'Hatchet' by Gary Paulsen. It is a story about a boy, Brian, who is stranded alone in the Canadian wilderness and has to survive until he is eventually rescued.

He turned back to his campsite and looked at the wreckage. He had a lot to do, rebuild his shelter, get a new fire going, find some food or get ready to find some food, make weapons – and he had to work slowly because his ribs hurt.

First things first. He tried to find some dry grass and twigs, then peeled bark from a nearby birch to shred into a fire nest. He worked slowly but even so, with his new skill he had a fire going in less than an hour. The flames cut the cool damp morning, crackled and did much to bring his spirits up, not to mention chasing away the incessant mosquitoes. With the fire going he searched for dry wood – the rain had driven water into virtually all the wood he could find – and at last located some in a thick evergreen where the top branches had covered the lower dead ones, keeping them dry.

He had great difficulty breaking them, not being able to pull much with his arm or chest muscles, but finally got enough to keep the fire going all day and into the night. With that he rested a bit, eased his chest, and then set about getting a shelter built.

Much of the wood from his original wall was still nearby and up at the back of the ridge he actually found a major section of weave still intact. The wind had torn it out, lifted it and thrown it to the top of the ridge and Brian felt lucky once more that he had not been killed or more seriously injured – which would have been the same, he thought. If he couldn't hunt he would die and if he were badly injured he would not be able to hunt.

He jerked and dragged wood around until the wall was once more in place – crudely, but he could improve it later. He had no trouble finding enough pine boughs to make a new bed. The storm had torn the forest to pieces – up behind the ridge it looked as if a giant had become angry and used some kind of a massive mincer on the trees. Huge pines were twisted and snapped off, blown sideways. The ground was so littered with limbs and tree-tops sticking every which way, that it was hard to get through. He pulled enough thick limbs in for a bed, green and spicy with the new broken sap smell, and by evening he was exhausted, hungry and hurting, but he had something close to a place to live in again, a place to be.

Andrew Brodie: Improving Comprehension for ages 9-10 © A&C Black Publishers Ltd 2008

Building a shelter

Name: _____

Date: _____

Ring the correct answers to the questions.

1. The main character in the book is called

   Byron   Bryson   Brian   Bradley

2. His campsite had been wrecked by

   a bomb   wild animals   an explosion   a storm

3. He used dry grass and twigs to start a

   fire   new home   tree   garden

Answer each of the next questions with a full sentence. The first one has been started for you.

4. Where is Brian stranded alone?

   Brian is stranded _____

   _____

   _____

5. Why did Brian feel lucky?

   _____

   _____

6. How did Brian feel by the evening?

   _____

   _____

7. What was the effect of the storm on the forest?

   _____

   _____

   _____

Notes for teachers
Before beginning to answer the questions on this page, ensure children understand the text. Pay particular attention to any unfamiliar words. You will need to check their understanding of the line 'he actually found a major section of weave still intact'. With the final three questions remind pupils to use complete sentences beginning with a capital letters and ending with a full stops.

Andrew Brodie: Improving Comprehension for ages 9-10 © A&C Black Publishers Ltd 2008

Building a shelter

Name: _____

Date: _____

Ring the correct answers to the questions.

1. Which word is nearest in meaning to 'original'?

    first   last   nearest   oldest

2. Which part of Brian was injured?

    legs   back   feet   chest

Answer each of the following questions with a full sentence.

3. What had wrecked the campsite?

    _____

    _____

4. How long did it take to get the fire going?

    _____

    _____

5. What did Brian need to build?

    _____

    _____

6. What did Brian make with pine boughs?

    _____

    _____

7. What do you think happened next? Use the lines below to jot down some ideas. As these are notes they do not need to be written in sentences.

    _____

    _____

    _____

    _____

Notes for teachers
Read the passage with the pupils and check they understand any unfamiliar words. Point out that the last task should be answered in note form. An extension activity would be to ask pupils to re-read the text and then draw what they think the area looked like.

Andrew Brodie: Improving Comprehension for ages 9-10 © A&C Black Publishers Ltd 2008

Building a shelter

Name: _____

Date: _____

Ring the correct answers to the question.

1. Which word is nearest in meaning to 'incessant'?

    continual   annoying   large   biting

Use complete sentences to answer the questions below.

2. In the text it says that the flames of his newly built fire 'did much to bring his spirits up'. Explain in your own words what is meant by this.

    _____

    _____

3. Why did Brian have difficulty breaking up pieces of firewood?

    _____

    _____

4. What had the storm done to the countryside?

    _____

    _____

5. Why did Brian feel that being seriously injured would have been as bad as being killed?

    _____

    _____

    _____

6. Explain what is meant in the text by 'The ground was so littered with limbs'.

    _____

    _____

    _____

Notes for teachers
Ensure the children have read and understood the passage, paying particular attention to any unfamiliar words.
When discussing the final question encourage pupils to realise that there is a link between 'limbs on a body'
and 'limbs on a tree' in that they are attached to the main trunk or body.

Andrew Brodie: Improving Comprehension for ages 9-10 © A&C Black Publishers Ltd 2008

The Jumblies (Part 1)

This is the first half of a nonsense poem, written by the Victorian writer Edward Lear, called 'The Jumblies'.

1
They went to see in a Sieve, they did,
In a Sieve they went to sea:
In spite of all their friends could say,
On a winter's morn, on a stormy day,
In a Sieve they went to sea
And when the Sieve turned round and round,
And everyone cried, 'You'll all be drowned!'
They called aloud, 'Our Sieve ain't big,
But we don't care a button! We don't care a fig!
In a sieve we'll go to sea!'
Far and few, far and few,
Are the lands where the Jumblies live
Their heads are green, and their hands are blue,
And they went to sea in a sieve.

2
They sailed away in a Sieve they did,
In a sieve they sailed so fast,
With only a beautiful pea-green veil
Tied with a riband by way of a sail,
To a small tobacco pipe mast;
And everyone said, who saw them go,
'O won't they soon be upset, you know!
For the sky is dark, and the voyage is long,
And happen what may, it's extremely wrong
In a sieve to sail so fast!'
Far and few, far and few,
Are the lands where the Jumblies live;
Their heads are green, and their hands are blue,
And they went to sea in a Sieve.

3
The water it soon came in, it did,
The water it soon came in;
So to keep them dry, they wrapped their feet
In a pinky paper all folded neat,
And they fastened it down with a pin.
And they passed the night in a crockery-jar,
And each of them said, "How wise we are!
Thought the sky be dark, and the voyage be long,
Yet we never can think we are rash or wrong,
While round in our sieve we spin!'
Far and few, far and few,
Are the lands where the Jumblies live;
Their heads are green, and their hands are blue,
And they went to sea in a Sieve.

Andrew Brodie: Improving Comprehension for ages 9-10 © A&C Black Publishers Ltd 2008

The Jumblies (Part 1)

Name: _____

Date: _____

Ring the correct answer for each of the following three questions.

1. What is the title of the poem?

    The Jimblies   The Jumblies   The Junglies   The Jubblies

2. What colour were their heads?

    pea green   blue   green   silver

3. What did they wrap in pinky paper?

    feet   heads   hands   sieve

Answer each of the following questions with a simple sentence. The first one has been started for you.

4. In what did the Jumblies go to sea?

    The Jumblies went to sea _____

    _____

5. From what was the mast made?

    _____

    _____

6. At what time of year did the Jumblies go to sea?

    _____

    _____

7. On a separate piece of paper draw and colour a picture of the Jumblies at sea in their sieve. Read the poem carefully to make sure that your picture includes the correct colours.

Notes for teachers

Read the poem together and enjoy the rhyme and rhythm. Are there any words the pupils don't understand? Ensure pupils include lots of detail and that they depict appropriate colours for a stormy day when completing the final task. They will need to read the poem to help them.

Name: _____

Date: _____

Ring the correct answer for each of the following questions.

1. In what did the Jumblies pass the night?

   a sieve   a storm   a crockery jar   a pea green veil

2. With what did the Jumblies fasten the pinky paper?

   tape   riband   mast   pin

Write a full sentence to answer each of the following questions.

3. Why would it actually be quite ridiculous to go out to sea in a sieve?

   _____

   _____

4. Which line of the poem tells you that their friends didn't think that sailing to sea in a sieve was a very good idea?

   _____

   _____

5. What did they do to keep their feet dry when the water came in?

   _____

   _____

6. Write the lines that are identical in every verse.

   _____

   _____

   _____

   _____

   _____

   _____

Notes for teachers
Where pupils are asked to use their own words they should be encouraged to check spellings for accuracy. When copying part of a verse in the final question, pupils should concentrate on careful presentation and correct spelling.

Andrew Brodie: Improving Comprehension for ages 9-10 © A&C Black Publishers Ltd 2008

The Jumblies (Part 1)

Name: _____

Date: _____

Ring the correct answer for each of the following questions.

1. What is meant by the word 'riband'?

    string   ribbon   tape   fabric

Write full sentences answer the following questions.

2. How big might you expect a Jumbly to be? Give reasons for your answer.

    _____

    _____

    _____

3. Name five things that help you to realise that this is a nonsense poem.

    _____

    _____

    _____

    _____

    _____

4. How many verses are there in the whole poem? Explain how you know this.

    _____

    _____

    _____

    _____

5. Can you write an extra verse of the poem, on a separate piece of paper?
    Try to follow the rhyming pattern of the original poem.

Notes for teachers

Read the poem with the children. If they are good readers then you could take it in turn to read a couple of lines each. Discuss any words the children are unfamiliar with. They might need some support with explaining the rhyming pattern. Encourage the children to look closely at the rhyming pattern. A helpful technique is to highlight or link the rhyming words in each verse.

Andrew Brodie: Improving Comprehension for ages 9-10 © A&C Black Publishers Ltd 2008

The Jumblies (Part 2)

This is the second part of Edward Lear's 'The Jumblies'. The author, who lived from 1812 to 1888, is probably best known for 'The Owl and the Pussycat' and his many limericks.

4

And all night long they sailed away;
And when the sun went down,
They whistled and warbled a moony song
To the echoing sound of a coppery gong,
In the shade of the mountains brown.
'O Timballo how happy we are,
When we live in a Sieve and a crockery jar.
And all night long in the moonlight pale,
We sail away with a pea green sail,
In the shade of the mountains brown!'
Far and few, far and few,
Are the lands where the Jumblies live;
Their heads are green, and their hands are blue,
And they went to sea in a Sieve.

5

They sailed to the Western Sea, they did,
To a land all covered with trees,
And they bought an Owl, and a useful Cart,
And a pound of Rice, and a Cranberry Tart,
And a hive of silvery Bees.
And they bought a Pig, and some green Larrydaws,
And a lovely monkey with lollipop paws,
And forty bottles of Ring-Bo-Ree,
And no end of Stilton Cheese.
Far and few, far and few,
Are the lands where the Jumblies live;
Their heads are green, and their hands are blue,
And they went to sea in a Sieve.

6

And in twenty years they all came back,
In twenty years or more,
And everyone said, "How tall they've grown!
For they've been to the Lakes, and the Terrible Zone,
And the hills of the Chankly Bore;"
And they drank their health, and gave them a feast
Of dumplings made of beautiful yeast;
And everyone said, "If we only live,
We too will go to sea in a Sieve –
To the hills of the Chankly Bore!"
Far and few, far and few,
Are the lands where the Jumblies live;
Their heads are green, and their hands are blue,
And they went to sea in a Sieve.

Andrew Brodie: Improving Comprehension for ages 9-10 © A&C Black Publishers Ltd 2008

The Jumblies (Part 2)

Name: _____

Date: _____

Ring the correct answer for each of the following three questions.

1. What colour was it in the shade of the mountains?

    green   brown   black   pea green

2. How many bottles of Ring-Bo-Ree did they buy?

    ten   twenty   thirty   forty

3. What did the Chankly Bore have?

    hills   mountains   valleys   streams

Each of the following questions should be answered with a simple sentence. The first one has been started for you.

4. What colour was the sail of their boat?

    The sail of their boat _____

5. Which two birds are mentioned in verse two?

    _____

    _____

6. How long did their voyage last?

    _____

    _____

7. In the box below draw and label the land they found in verse two. Include the things they bought there. Read verse 2 again. Write about the things that were bought.

    _____

    _____

Notes for teachers

Read the poem together and talk about any unfamiliar words. See if the children can work out what they mean from the context. Encourage pupils to talk about their drawings.

The Jumblies (Part 2)

Name: _____

Date: _____

1. For which other type of poem is Edward Lear well known?

   ode   sonnet   limerick   nursery rhyme

2. Which words describe the way the Jumblies made their song?

   whistled and hummed   warbled and woofed

   echoed and warbled   whistled and warbled

3. Ring the word nearest in meaning to 'pale'.

   shiny   weak   silver   bright

Write a full sentence to answer each of the following questions.

4. To which sea did the Jumblies sail?

   _____

   _____

5. What did they find when they got there?

   _____

   _____

6. How is the monkey described?

   _____

   _____

7. What had changed about the Jumblies when they returned home?

   _____

   _____

   _____

Notes for teachers

Read and enjoy the poem together. Discuss with the pupils the main events of Part 1 and then how the poem comes to a conclusion in Part 2. When answering the question about the monkeys, pupils should include both the 'lollipop paws' and the word 'lovely'. Where pupils are asked to use their own words they should be encouraged to check spellings for accuracy.

Andrew Brodie: Improving Comprehension for ages 9-10 © A&C Black Publishers Ltd 2008

The Jumblies (Part 2)

Name: _____

Date: _____

Write a full sentences to answer each of the following questions.

1. How do the first two lines of verse 4 remind you this is a nonsense poem?

   _____

   _____

   _____

2. Write the words that the Jumblies whistled and warbled in their song.

   _____

   _____

   _____

   _____

3. Name four places visited by the Jumblies on their voyage.

   _____

   _____

4. How were the Jumblies welcomed home?

   _____

   _____

   _____

5. After returning from their voyage would it be correct to say that the Jumblies had started a trend? Explain your answer.

   _____

   _____

   _____

Notes for teachers

For the questions that ask pupils to explain their understanding of the text, they should make their answers as detailed as possible. Question 1 refers to verse 4. Pupils may need to be reminded that this is in fact the first verse of this text. The second question requires pupils to write 5 lines of the poem and ideally these should be presented as shown in the text. In tackling the final question pupils should show that they have an understanding of the phrase 'started a trend' within their answer.